Contents

*C = copper; B = bronze; T = teacher; ( ) = the line must be played but cannot be assessed for a Medal.

Rain Dance

Kathy and David Blackwell

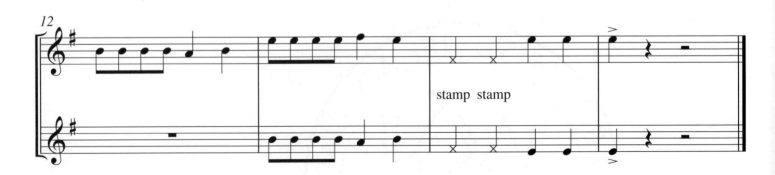

AB 3014

Do have a cup of tea!

Sheila Nelson

*Do have a cup of | tea! No thank you. | Just half a cup with | me? I hate it!

(Make up the rest of the words.)

* Sing or speak the words before you learn the piece, then think the words as you play.

Mirrors

Edward Huws Jones

AB 3014

Would you like some beans on toast?

Mary Cohen

* The words are to help with the rhythm in rehearsal, but are not intended to be performed.

Water's Edge

Katherine and Hugh Colledge

Gently, with lots of bow ♩ = *c.*100

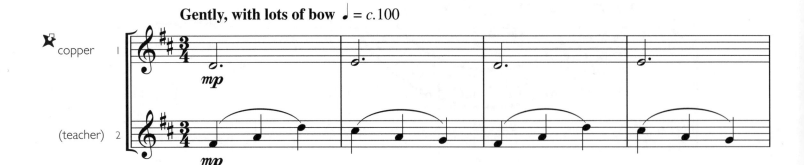

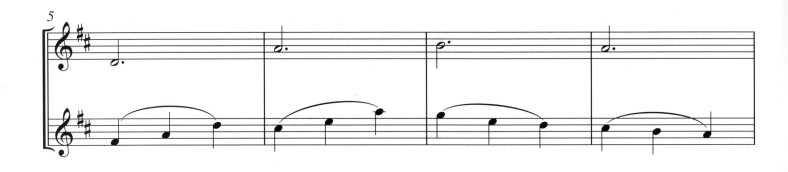

AB 3014

Song of the Weavers

Mary Cohen

Danger Signal!

Edward Huws Jones

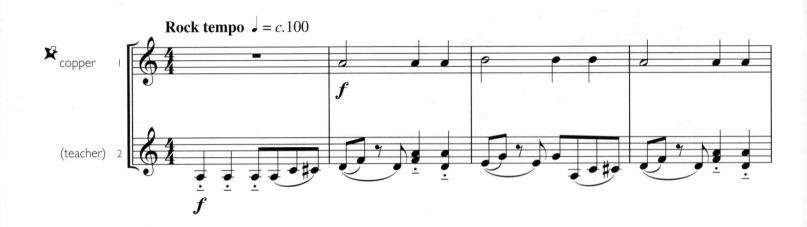

* DAN-GER SIG-NAL! DAN-GER SIG-NAL!

DAN-GER SIG-NAL! DAN-GER SIG-NAL!

* Shout the words as you play. For the Medal this is optional.

Little Star!

Anthony Marks

An Argument

Katie Wearing

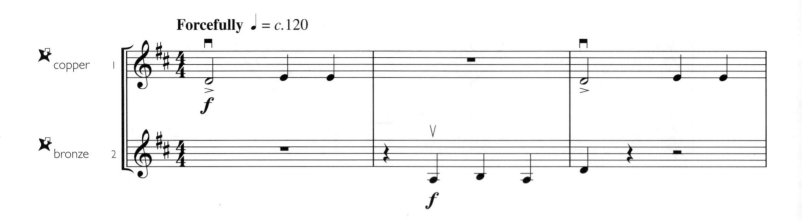

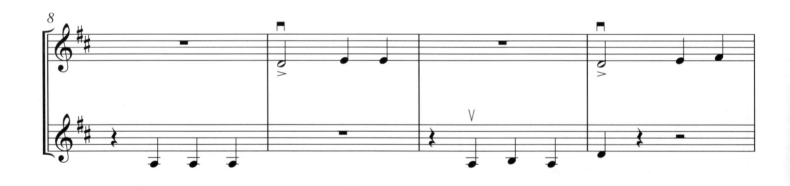

AB 3014

Hoedown

Kathy and David Blackwell

I can play louder than you can

Polly Waterfield

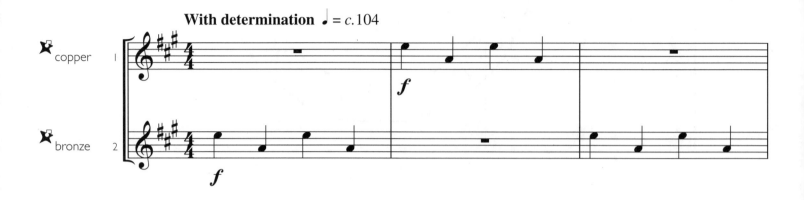

AB 3014

Country Gardens

Trad. English arr. Mary Cohen

Star of the County Down

Trad. arr. Edward Huws Jones

AB 3014

Riding the Carousel

Mary Cohen

AB 3014